DISNEY · PIXAR
FINDING NEMO

Nemo in School

Level 1

Re-told by: Melanie Williams
Series Editor: Rachel Wilson

Before You Read

In This Book

Nemo

Marlin

Mr. Ray

Activity

Read and say. What is Nemo?

1 a cat
2 a fish
3 a dog

This is Nemo. He's a fish.

This is his dad. His name is Marlin.

They live in the ocean.

Hooray! Hooray! Nemo is happy.

It's his first day in school today!

Where's the school?

It's there.

Where are the teachers?
Are they the teachers?

No, they're the moms and dads.

Nemo has new friends at school.
Pearl, Tad and Sheldon are nice.

They play in the ocean.

This is Mr. Ray. He's the teacher.
Where's the new class?

They're here! Hello, class.

They have fun in school!
Bye, moms and dads.

After You Read

1 **Match the words and the pictures.**

1 Marlin
2 teacher
3 friends

2 **Read and say Yes or No.**

1 Nemo lives at school.
2 The school is in the ocean.
3 It's the first day of school.
4 Mr. Ray is the dad.
5 Nemo has some new friends.

Picture Dictionary

mom

dad

friends

have fun

ocean

school

teacher

class

Phonics

Say the sounds. Read the words.

M m

Marlin

mom

N n

Nemo

I'm Noah.

name

Say the tongue twister.

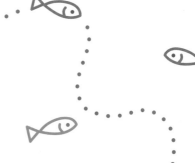

His name is Nemo.
He is new.
His name is Marlin.
He is nice.

Values

Make new friends at school.

Find Out

What lives on the coral reef?

This is the Great Barrier Reef. It's a coral reef.
It's in Australia. Many fish live on the reef.
The colors are beautiful!

coral reef

Australia

Great Barrier Reef

Pearson Education Limited
KAO Two
KAO Park, Harlow,
Essex, CM17 9NA, England
and Associated Companies throughout the world.

ISBN: 978-1-2923-4664-9

This edition first published by Pearson Education Ltd 2020

12

Set in Heinemann Roman Special, 19pt/28pt
Printed by Ashford Colour Press Ltd

Published by Pearson Education Limited

Acknowledgments
123RF.com: eklervector 21
Getty Images: Jeff Hunter 20-21
Shutterstock.com: 17, 18, HTeam 18, pyzata 17

For a complete list of the titles available in the Pearson English Readers series, visit www.pearsonenglishreaders.com.

Alternatively, write to your local Pearson Education office or to Pearson English Readers Marketing Department, Pearson Education, KAO Two, KAO Park, Harlow, Essex, CM17 9NA